Letterland

Things to Make & Do

Published by Letterland International Ltd, Leatherhead, Surrey, KT22 9AD, UK

www.letterland.com

© Letterland International 2013
This edition published 2013.
ISBN: 978-1-86209-916-6
10 9 8 7 6 5 4 3 2 1

Letterland® is a registered trademark of Lyn Wendon.
Author: Sarah Edwards
Originator of Letterland: Lyn Wendon
Designer: Sarah Edwards
Photography – iStockphoto.com. Cover image © Wojciech Gajda

British Library Cataloguing in Publication Data
A catalogue record for this publication is available from the British Library

Printed in Singapore

Contents

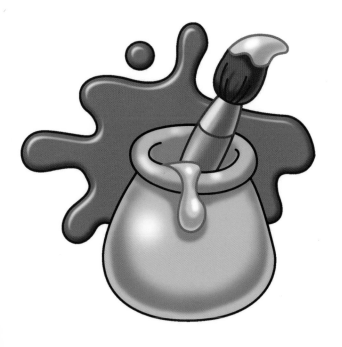

Introduction

An A-Z of craft and play ideas

This book is full of great things to make and do with crafty ways to learn as you go!

There is no better way to learn than when it happens naturally. While you are following the step-by-step craft activities or playing games together, opportunities to talk and learn will simply present themselves.

- talk about the shapes, textures and colours of materials used,
- talk about different sounds you hear as you follow each project,
- learn new vocabulary to describe how to make each craft,
- look out for the alliterative language for each letter of the alphabet.

There are lots more ideas for developing language skills in the back of this book, as well as information about Letterland - the educational publisher of phonics books, that help children become happy, confident and successful in early literacy and in life!

Safety first!

It is most important that all the crafts and games are completed safely and your house remains the way you like it! Look out for these symbols throughout.

Paints and Glue
Cover surfaces with newspaper and wear aprons. We advise the use of non-toxic PVA glue and washable poster paints.

Scissors
We advise the use of safety scissors, or if your child is very young, do any cutting required for them.

Warning
Read the additional advice given and take extra care where you see this symbol.

Supervision
Where you see this symbol, adult supervision may be required.

4

This book contains creative crafts and games for every letter of the alphabet to stimulate your child's imagination. Each page has step-by-step instructions, colourful illustrations, at-a-glance guides to required materials and difficulty ratings.

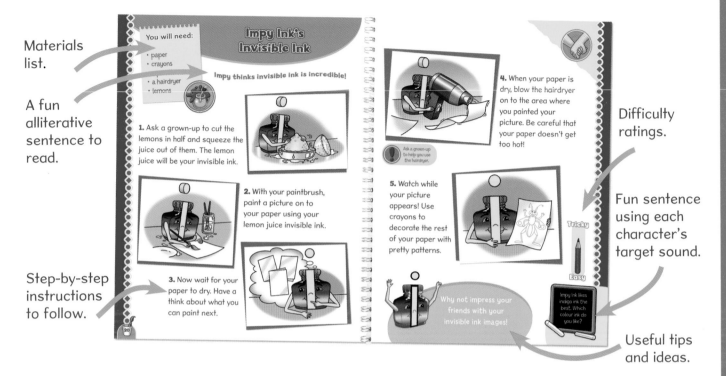

Materials list.

A fun alliterative sentence to read.

Step-by-step instructions to follow.

Difficulty ratings.

Fun sentence using each character's target sound.

Useful tips and ideas.

NB: We have used metric measurements in this book. As a guide, 2.5cm = 1".

Things you'll need!

Before you start each project, look at the list of the things you need in the top left-hand corner of each page spread. You may already have most things at home. You can recycle lots of household products, too. Use thin card from old cereal boxes, yogurt pots to mix paint or use as glue pots and plastic lids for paint palettes. You can also re-use your tissue paper and wrapping paper.
Some of the ideas in this book only need your child to have lots of energy!

Get creative!

Paint, paste and play!

You will need:

- a dice
- 18 small paper squares
- a friend to play with!

Annie loves animals and adventures!

Tricky

Easy

ant   **antelope**   **bat**

Take it in turns to throw a dice. Using the **map key**, cover one picture square on your map that matches the number you rolled. The first person to cover all their squares wins!

Map key:

If you throw a 1, cover a...

If you throw a 2, cover a...

If you throw a 3, cover a...

If you throw a 4, cover a...

If you throw a 5, cover an...

If you throw a 6, cover an...

Can you find Annie Apple's 'a' shape in all the animal's names? What animal do you like best?

camel   **cat**   **lamb**

You will need:

- paper
- coloured paints
- a bowl
- washing-up liquid
- a straw

Bouncy Ben's Butterflies and Bubbles

Ben thinks being busy is brilliant!

1. Fold a piece of paper in half. Then open it out again. Put several big blobs of paint on one half of the paper.

2. Now fold your paper along the crease and press down all over.

3. Unfold your paper and paint on eyes and feelers. You've made a beautiful butterfly picture!

1. Mix some washing-up liquid and some paint in a bowl.

Take care not to swallow any of the mixture.

2. Carefully blow into the mixture with a straw until you have lots of bubbles.

3. Gently press a piece of paper on top of the bubbles then lift it off. Look at the bubble picture you have made!

Tricky

Easy

Look outside at the butterflies. Can you spot any that have blue on them?

You will need:

- paper
- paint, pens or crayons
- a friend or two!

Clever Cat loves creating her creatures!

1. Take a piece of paper each and draw a head at the top. Make it as funny as you like!

2. Fold the paper over to hide the head you've drawn. Swap papers with your friend. Leave a tiny bit of the neck showing so that your friend knows where to start drawing the body.

3. Now draw a body and arms. Is your crazy creature fat or thin? What colour is its body? How many arms does it have?

4. Fold your paper over to hide the body you've drawn and swap with your friend.

5. Now draw some legs, then swap papers again and draw some feet. When you've finished, open up the paper to look at the crazy creature you've made!

Tricky

Easy

Can you decide which is the craziest creature you've created?!

Count how many creatures you can think of that start with Clever Cat's 'c' sound?

Dippy Duck's Disco Dance

You will need:

• lots of energy!

Sing this song to the tune of 'The wheels on the bus...'

Dippy Duck loves to disco dance all day!

1. Dippy Duck's dance goes flap, flap, flap,
flap, flap, flap,
flap, flap, flap,
Dippy Duck's dance goes flap, flap, flap!
All day long!

Flap your arms like wings.

2. Dippy Duck's dance goes whoosh, whoosh, whoosh...

Twirl round in a circle.

Shake your tail like Dippy!

3. Dippy Duck's dance goes wiggle, wiggle, wiggle...

4. Dippy Duck's dance goes quack, quack, quack...

Make a beak with your hands.

5. Dippy Duck's dance goes splash, splash, splash...

Kick your feet up in the air.

Do all the actions at once!

6. Dippy Duck's dance goes flap, flap, flap, whoosh, whoosh, whoosh, wiggle, wiggle, wiggle, quack, quack, quack, splash, splash, splash! All day long!

Tricky

Easy

Do you like to dance? How many different dance moves can you do?

You will need:

- cress seeds
- egg shells
- cotton wool
- a felt-tip pen
- egg cups
- water

Eddy's egg heads are egg-cellent!

1. Save the shell from a boiled egg and line it with damp cotton wool.

2. Draw a happy face on the shell with a felt-tip pen.

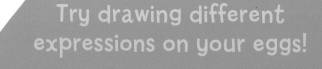
Try drawing different expressions on your eggs!

14

3. Carefully scatter cress seeds into the shell. The seeds will grow and become the eggs' hair.

4. Place your eggs on a window sill where they can get some light.

Tricky

5. Add a small amount of water every day and watch your egg heads' hair grow!

Easy

Eddy knows eleven ways of cooking eggs! How many can you think of?

You will need:

- paper
- coloured paints
- a paintbrush
- scissors
- thin card
- glue

These make fabulous gifts for your family.

1. Carefully paint your hand and fingers. Make a handprint on the paper. Do this lots of times and with different coloured paints. Make sure the handprints don't overlap! Now let the paint dry.

Don't forget to wash your hands now!

2. When the handprints are dry, carefully cut around them, taking extra care when cutting around the fingers.

3. Cut a circle, 14cm in diameter, from the card. Then cut another circle, 10cm in diameter, from the middle. This will be the back of your frame.

4. Glue your handprints around the edge of the card frame. Make sure that the fingers are pointing outwards and the prints overlap.

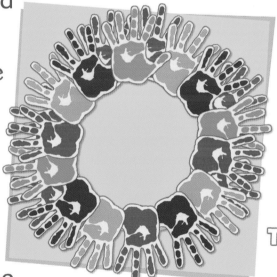

5. Continue sticking your handprints around the edge. When you've gone all round the circle your frame is complete.

Tricky

Easy

6. Stick a photograph on to the back. Now your funky frame is a fantastic gift for your family or friends!

Firefighter Fred has five people in his family. Can you count how many people are in your family?

You will need:

- a dice
- a counter for each player
- a friend or two!

Golden Girl thinks games are great!

1. Put your counters on the 'start' square.
2. Roll the dice and move that number.

START

a   b   c   d

j   k   l   m   n

s   t   u   v   w

3. Describe an animal that starts with the letter sound that you've landed on. If you can't think of one, miss a turn.

4. The first player to guess the animal correctly has the next turn.

5. The winner is the first person to reach the finish square.

e f g h i

o p q r

Tricky

Easy

x y z **FINISH**

For the letter 'x', you'll need to think of a word with 'x' at the **end**, like ox or fox.

Golden Girl likes goats. Can you think of other animals that start with Golden Girl's 'g' sound?

Harry Hat Man's Happy Heads

Harry thinks happy heads are hilarious!

1. Put the bread rolls on a work surface. Cut them in half. Then flatten them gently and evenly all over using a rolling pin.

2. Spread each half with pizza topping.

20

3. Stamp out some shapes in the cheese for eyes. Use a mushroom for the nose and pepper slices for the mouth.

Take care not to eat the happy heads until they're cool.

4. Ask a grown-up to cook the happy heads under a hot grill until the cheese has melted.

Tricky

Easy

Harry Hat Man likes healthy foods. What healthy food do you like best?

What other toppings could you use to make Harry's happy heads?

You will need:

- paper
- crayons
- a paintbrush
- a hairdryer
- lemons

Impy thinks invisible ink is incredible!

1. Ask a grown-up to cut the lemons in half and squeeze the juice out of them. The lemon juice will be your invisible ink.

2. With your paintbrush, paint a picture on to your paper using your lemon juice invisible ink.

3. Now wait for your paper to dry. Have a think about what you can paint next.

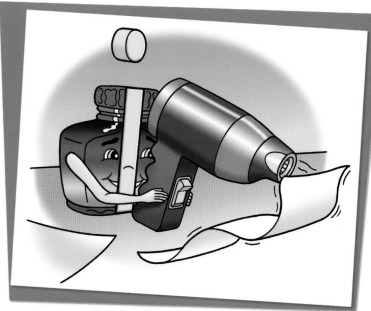

4. When your paper is dry, blow the hairdryer on to the area where you painted your picture. Be careful that your paper doesn't get too hot!

Ask a grown-up to help you use the hairdryer.

5. Watch while your picture appears! Use crayons to decorate the rest of your paper with pretty patterns.

Tricky

Easy

Why not impress your friends with your invisible ink images!

Impy Ink likes indigo ink the best. Which colour ink do you like?

Jumping Jim's Jangly Jewellery

You will need:

- string
- pasta tubes
- a paintbrush
- coloured paints

Jim's jewellery makes him jump for joy!

1. Cut a length of string. Make sure it's at least twice the length you want your finished jangly jewellery to be. Arrange the pasta beside the string to see if you have enough to cover it.

2. Paint the pasta with your brightest paints.

24

3. When the paint is dry, thread the coloured pasta shapes on to the string. When you have used up all the pasta, tie the ends of the string.

Always take care when using string.

Make sure there is enough room for the pasta shapes to move up and down so they make the jingly-jangly noise that Jumping Jim enjoys!

Tricky

Easy

Jumping Jim likes to juggle jellies when he jumps. Can you juggle and jump?

Kicking King's Key Fob

You will need:

- 1 cup plain flour
- 1/2 cup salt
- 1/4 cup water
- mixing bowl
- cling film
- rolling pin
- round edged knife
- baking tray
- paintbrushes
- acrylic paints & varnish

Keep your keys safe like Kicking King!

1. Mix the salt and flour in a bowl. Add the water and knead the mixture until it becomes smooth and elastic. Cover the dough with cling film and let it rest for 30 minutes.

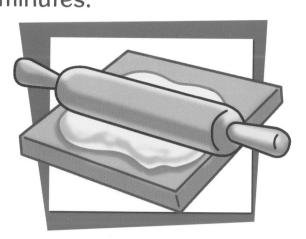

2. Preheat the oven to 120°C. Roll out the dough so that it's about 10mm thick.

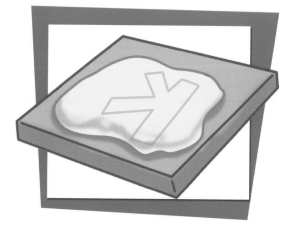

3. Draw a letter shape in the dough. Cut round the shape.

Always ask a grown-up to heat the oven. Do not eat the dough!

4. Once your shape is created make a small hole near the top. You could also put patterns on your letter with a pencil or cocktail stick.

5. Carefully place the dough letter shape on the baking tray and bake for about two and a half hours. Remove from the oven and allow to cool completely.

6. Decorate with acrylic paints and allow to dry. Then finish with a coat of clear varnish.

Tricky

Easy

7. Tie a ribbon through the hole. If you made Kicking King's 'k' you could make an 'e' and a 'y' to spell out the word 'key'!

Kicking King keeps his keys on his key fob. What else could you keep on yours?

your key fob is ready!

Lucy Lamp Light's Lotto

You will need:

- two dice
- counters or coins
- friends to play with!

Lucy loves her lucky lotto game!

Tricky

Easy

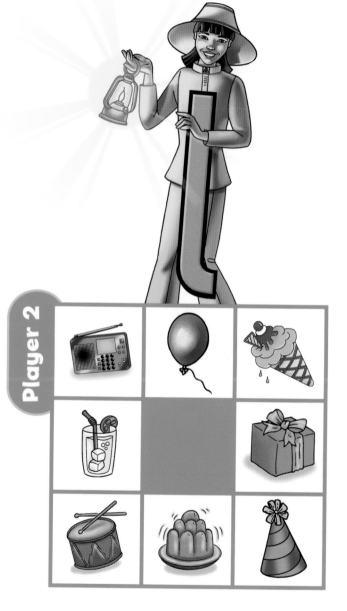

Player 1

Player 2

2	3	4	5	6	7

1. Each player chooses a player grid.

2. Take it in turns to throw both dice. Add the numbers together.

3. Check which picture matches the total number you've thrown.

4. If you have that picture, cover it with a counter. The winner is the first person to cover all their pictures and shout, 'Lucy's lotto!'

Player 3

Player 4

8

9

10

11

12

Lucy Lamp Light likes licking a lollipop while she plays lotto! Do you like lollipops?

Munching Mike's Magic Mobile

Mike's magic mobiles are magnificent!

1. Stick the dots onto each plastic cup to make a 'key pad' for your telephone. Write numbers 0-9 on the dots.

2. Ask a grown-up to make a small hole in the bottom of each cup.

3. Thread the ends of the string through the holes in the cups. Tie a large knot in the end of each string.

4. Give one cup to a friend and ask them to walk away until the string is stretched tight.

 Always take care when using string.

5. Ask your friend to hold their cup to their ear as you speak into yours.

Now you can talk to your friend!

Tricky

Easy

Mike mentions...

The telephone works well when the string is stretched tight and straight. Hold the cups at the rim so that the bottoms are free to vibrate.

Mmmarvellous!

Munching Mike likes making music as well as magic mobiles! Do you like music, too?

Noisy Nick's Noughts and Crosses

You will need:

• 10 round stickers
• a pen or crayon
• counters or card circles
• a friend to play with!

Nick is really noisy when he plays this!

1. Draw 5 noughts and 5 crosses on your stickers.

2. Stick the noughts and crosses on your counters.

3. Choose which player will be noughts and which will be crosses.

4. The first player places a counter in one of the squares on the grid opposite.

5. The first player to get three in a row, up, down, across or diagonally, wins!

Tricky

Easy

It's Nick that wins!

Make more counters with pictures that start with Noisy Nick's sound.

nest

nut

nail

Playing noughts and crosses is nnnice!

noodles

What else could you draw?

Noisy Nick played this new game nine times! Have you played it nine times yet?

You will need:

- scissors
- a pen
- thin card or paper
- two cups or hats
- friends to play with!

Oscar can't stop playing this game!

1. Write down the opposite words and action words below on paper or thin card (or ask a grown-up to help). Then carefully cut a rectangle around each word.

2. Find two cups or hats. Put all the opposite cards in one cup and all the action cards in the other.

Opposites!

forwards   backwards

quickly   slowly   quietly   noisily

3. Take it in turns to pick out an action and an opposite. Do whatever it says on the action card in the way it tells you on the opposite card. For example, you might get walk and slow, dance and quickly or crawl and backwards! See if you can do it!

Dance quickly like Oscar!

Tricky

Can you think of any more opposites you could use in Oscar Orange's game?

Easy

Oscar Orange says on and off are opposites, too. How many opposite words can you think of?

Actions!

walk   run   crawl

hop   roll   skip   dance   jump

You will need:
- thin card
- scissors
- wool
- felt/coloured paper
- glue
- pipe cleaner
- googly eyes

Peter's pom-poms pets are perfect!

1. Cut out four card circles – one large pair (about 7cm diameter) and one small pair (about 5cm diameter). Cut out smaller circles from the centres to make four rings.

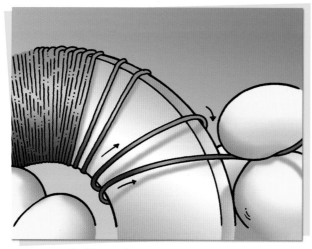

2. Put the large circles together and wind the wool around them. Wind it tightly so that there are no gaps between the wool.

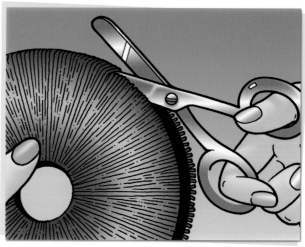

3. When the wool is wrapped around the circles thickly, cut the wool between the cardboard circles.

4. Tie a piece of wool between the two rings and pull it tightly around the middle. Gently pull off the card circles. Now make the small pom-pom in the same way.

To make a pom-pom cat...

Glue your pom-poms together. Cut two triangles from the felt or coloured paper for ears and glue them to the head. Stick on two googly eyes and a cardboard triangle for its nose. Glue on the pipe cleaner as the tail.

Tricky

Easy

Now you could make some more pom-pom pets. Here are some ideas for you to try!

⭐ **Rabbit** – two pom-poms (as before) and one very small white pom-pom for its tail, some felt ears and two eyes.

⭐ **Spider** – One black pom-pom, black pipe cleaners for legs, two googly eyes.

⭐ **Chicken** – two yellow pom-poms (as before), two eyes and an orange triangle for a beak.

Peter Puppy loves his pom-pom pets. Have you got any pets?

You will need:

- thin card
- scissors
- sticky tape
- PVA glue
- coloured tissue paper

The Queen's crown is quite quirky!

1. Wrap the card around your head and mark the place where it meets.

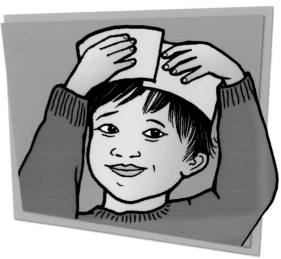

2. Carefully cut out a crown shape.

3. Fasten the ends of the crown together with sticky tape or glue.

4. Scrunch up tissue paper to make jewels. Stick them to your crown with PVA glue.

Why not make a quirky crown for your friend?

Tricky

Easy

You could use shells, jewels or sequins to decorate your quirky crown.

Quarrelsome Queen likes to be quiet. Can you think of things that are quiet?

Red Robot's Exercise Routine

You will need:

- lots of energy!

Red Robot says, "Ready, steady, GO!"

Red Robot really likes running!

1. Reach out with your right hand. Now reach out with your left. Repeat ten times!

Reach!

Roll!

2. Are you ready? Put your hands down and roll forwards... then repeat ten times!

3. Reach for your toes. Can you touch them? Reach to your right then reach to your left. Repeat ten times!

Reach!

Run!

4. Ready, steady, run! Run on the spot for one minute!

Tricky

Easy

Red Robot thinks you've done really well with his routine!

Red Robot runs and rolls regularly. Can you think of an exercise where you rotate?

You will need:

- balloons
- tissue paper

Sammy Snake's snowstorm is superb!

1. Ask an adult to blow up a balloon. Make some 'snow' by tearing some tissue paper into little pieces.

2. Rub the balloon several times on your sweater. Rub it quite fast until the balloon tries to stick. It is now charged with static electricity.

3. Hold the balloon near your tissue paper 'snow'. Look what happens! Recharge your balloon and you can play with your snowstorm again!

4. Rub the balloon again to recharge it. Now see what happens if you hold it against someone's hair!

Tricky

Easy

Sammy says...

Static electricity is not dangerous, like real electricity. Never play with real electricity. Instead have fun making your own static electricity with a balloon, like this.

Sammy Snake thinks science is so much fun. He thinks his static snowstorm is super-special!

You will need:

- red, green and white felt
- scissors
- tracing paper
- pencil
- glue
- googly eyes

Tess makes her tomato puppet talk!

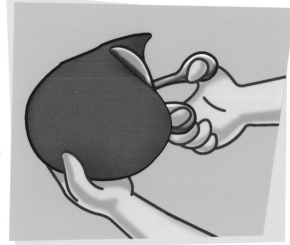

1. Cut two 10cm circles from the red felt.

2. Trace the shapes below on to tracing paper. Cut round the 'top' shape in green felt and the 'mouth' shape in white felt.

Trace shapes!

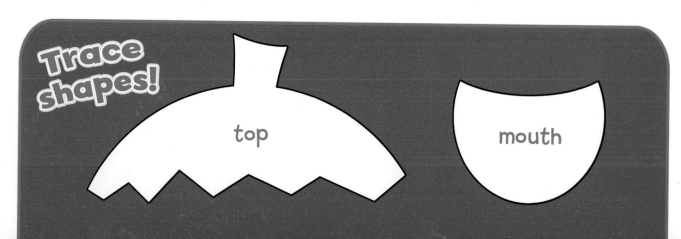

top

mouth

3. Glue round two-thirds of the edge of the red shapes and glue them together. The gap you leave will be the space for your fingers to go in!

4. Glue the green felt shape to the top of the red circles and the white mouth at the bottom, above the gap for your fingers.

5. Add on the googly eyes and let all the glue dry.

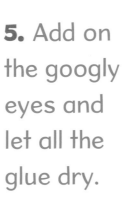

Tricky

Easy

Tess's Top Tip!

You can decorate your puppet, and make the edges stronger, by stitching the edges in colourful thread.

Talking Tess likes tasty tomatoes on toast for her tea. What do you like for your tea?

You will need:

- a small rock
- acrylic paint & varnish
- paintbrush
- PVA glue
- googly eyes, wool and a felt oval shape

Uppy thinks these ugly bugs are unusual!

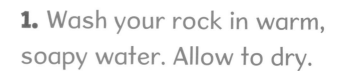

1. Wash your rock in warm, soapy water. Allow to dry.

2. Paint the rock completely with one colour. Leave to dry.

3. Now paint your bug's patterns - you could do spots or stripes or anything you'd like! Once this is dry, paint with varnish.

4. Glue the felt oval to the bottom of your ugly bug. This makes your bug's feet!

5. Glue on the googly eyes and wool hair. You can use felt to make the eyes and mouth if you prefer. Use your imagination to make your bug look really unusual!

You could make a whole family of ugly bugs! Uppy has given one to his Uncle Uppy!

Tricky

Easy

Put your drawings and colourings under your ugly bug for a fun paper weight!

Uppy Umbrella likes being upside-down! Can you turn upside-down?

Vicky Violet's Volcano

You will need:

- 6 cups plain flour
- 2 cups salt
- 4 tbsp oil
- 2 cups water
- bowl
- empty 500ml plastic bottle
- tray
- 4 tbsp warm water
- 2 heaped tbsp bicarbonate of soda
- 4 tbsp vinegar
- jug

Vicky's very excited about her volcano!

1. Mix the salt and flour in a bowl. Add the water and oil and knead the mixture until it becomes smooth and elastic. Cover the dough and let it rest for 30 minutes.

2. Stand the bottle on the tray. Press the dough to the outside of the bottle and mould it into a mountain shape. Don't cover the bottle opening!

3. Let the dough dry. Leave it at least four hours - overnight is best.

Do not eat the dough! Take extra care when creating the lava.

48

Now make your volcano erupt!

1. Mix the warm water and bicarbonate of soda together.

2. Pour the mixture into your volcano opening.

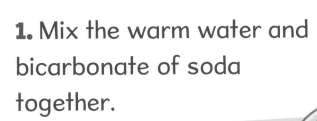

3. Pour the vinegar, all in one go, into the volcano. Watch your lava bubble up!

Tricky

Easy

Add food colouring to your lava mixture to make the volcano even more realistic! Orange and red work best!

The vinegar in Vicky Violet's volcano helps the lava erupt.

You will need:

- two strips of paper (approx 3 x 30cm)
- coloured card
- glue
- tracing paper
- scissors
- crayons or felt-tip pens

Walter's wobbly cards are wonderful!

1. Glue the ends of the long strips of paper together to make a corner shape.

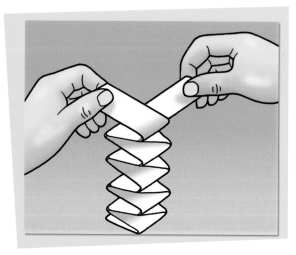

2. Fold the bottom strip over the top strip, and keep repeating. When you can't make any more folds, glue the ends together.

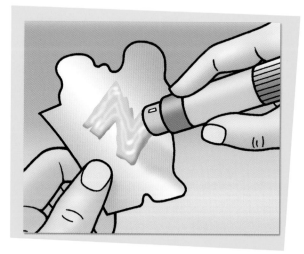

3. Now trace over the picture of Walter opposite, colour and cut it out. Then do another one. Glue one picture to one end of the spring.

4. Fold your piece of card in half. Stick the other picture of Walter to the front of your card.

5. Open your card up and glue the end of the spring to the inside. Now when you open the card, Walter Walrus will wobble out from the middle!

Try making some more wobbly cards with the other Letterlanders!

Tricky

Easy

Walter Walrus wobbles when he goes swimming! He thinks water is wonderful!

Trace shape!

Fix-it Max's Wax Work

You will need:

- paper
- coloured paints
- a paintbrush
- black wax crayons
- a coin

Max thinks these pictures are exciting!

1. Using your paints, cover the whole sheet of paper with lots of bright colours. Make sure that there are no white areas showing through. (If you prefer, you could use felt-tip pens instead.)

2. While you're waiting for the paint to dry, think about what picture you want to draw. Perhaps it could be something that contains Fix-it Max's sound, like a number six, a box or a fox.

3. When the paint is dry, colour over the top of it with a black wax

crayon. Make sure that you can't see any colours through the black.

4. Using the coin, gently scratch a picture into the black wax. The bright colours underneath will show where you've scratched off the wax. Now you've made an extra-special, wax work!

Tricky

Easy

Fix-it Max's favourite number is six. What number can you count up to?

You will need:
- a yo-yo
- lots of patience!

The Yo-yo Man says, "Yes, you can!"

The Throw Down

1. Hold the yo-yo palm up, standing it between your thumb and middle finger.

2. Whizz the yo-yo straight over, down to the ground. When the string reaches the end give a tug and the yo-yo will return back up.

The Sleeper

1. Hold your yo-yo in the same way as before.

2. Whip the yo-yo sharply toward the ground. It should stay down at the end of the string, spinning.

3. While it's spinning, turn your yo-yo hand over so that the palm faces down. Give the string a jerk. The yo-yo will return to your hand.

Tricky

Easy

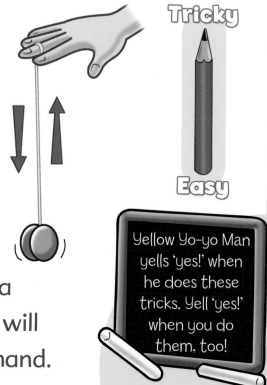

Yellow Yo-yo Man yells 'yes!' when he does these tricks. Yell 'yes!' when you do them, too!

You will need:

- paper (10cm x 10cm square)
- felt-tip pens
- scissors
- glue
- a stapler
- tin foil
- a split pin
- a drinking straw

Zig Zag watches these whizz round!

1. Write z's all over one side of the paper square.

2. Make four 8cm cuts towards the centre from each corner.

3. Bend the top right corner into the centre. Glue it down. Turn the paper and repeat for each of the four sides.

4. Carefully staple the points to the centre.

Tricky

Easy

5. Pack the top of a straw with scrunched up foil. Push the pin all the way through the zany zoom, straw and foil. Split the pin on the other side. Your zany zoom is ready!

Zzzany zoom!

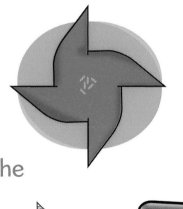

Zig Zag Zebra gets dizzy watching these whizz! Watch yours zoom!

Creating language
Letterland language fun!

There are lots of opportunities for speaking and listening while you make and do things together. Here are a few more ideas for accelerating the learning process with our child-friendly pictogram characters.

1. Living Alphabet – mould models of all the Letterland characters.

2. Character Costumes – make costumes or headbands for each of the Letterland characters. Costume ideas can be found on our website at **www.letterland.com/costumes**.

3. Alphabet Challenge – go through the alphabet saying the Letterland character, making the letter sound and think of a 'crafty' word that starts with their sound.

> **NOTE** the right sound is at the start of each Letterlander's name and in the Letterland Alphabet Songs.

Annie Apple says 'a'. She likes drawing animals.
Bouncy Ben says 'b'. He likes bursting balloons.
Clever Cat says 'c'. She likes creative crafts.

You can find lots of the Letterlander's songs on our website at **www.letterland.com/freesongs**.

4. Knock! Knock! – Play in pairs. Take turns to start.

A: Knock! knock!
B: Who's there?
A: I like scissors and sticky tape. Who am I?
B: Sammy Snake!

5. Label crazy – Put labels on all your craft supplies. Draw the correct Letterlander on the first letter to help you read and remember the words.

Take a look at the fantastic range of phonics products from Letterland at: www.letterland.com

Even more things to make and do with the Letterlanders!

Annie Apple - Apple Printing Cut apples across horizontally to show the 'star' pattern inside. Then make apple patterns with them by pressing them on to sponges full of paint.

Bouncy Ben - Building Bridges Use building blocks and build bridges together.

Clever Cat - Cat Collages Make cat collages by collecting cat pictures cut out from cards, calendars and magazines.

Dippy Duck - Dough Ducks Use modelling dough to make dough ducks just like Dippy.

Eddy Elephant - Exciting Eggs Paint and decorate hard boiled eggs.

Firefighter Fred - Fantastic Flames Make flame or fire pictures using red, yellow and orange finger paints and five fingers!

Golden Girl - Miniature Garden Grow a miniature garden, either using grass seed, moss, cress, flowers etc., or by making flowers out of modelling dough.

Harry Hat Man - Huge Handprints Draw a huge, hollow handprint on a piece of paper. Fill it with small handprints by painting your hands and pressing them into the huge handprint to fill the space.

Impy Ink - Ink Prints Get an ink pad and try making your own ink print picture with rubber stamps.

Jumping Jim - Jungle Tear green paper into loose leaf shapes. Thread them together with string and hang them from the ceiling to create a jungle effect.

Kicking King - Kitchen Collage Collect lots of pictures of things you'd find in the kitchen.

Lucy Lamp Light - Little Lambs Make some little lambs together, using cotton reels covered in cotton wool. Give them pipe cleaner legs.

Munching Mike - Monster Model Make a model of Munching Mike. Or maybe a picture of the metal monster using foil. Make sure he has three legs, not four!

Noisy Nick - Thank you Notes Make little notes out of card. Write 'thank you' and your name on them.

Oscar Orange - Object Game Place six objects on a tray. Close your eyes, then ask someone to put on or take off one object. Other players then name the object that has been put on or taken off.

Peter Puppy - Potato Printing Cut potatoes into a variety of shapes, including petal shapes and paw shapes. Make prints using pink and purple paint.

Quarrelsome Queen - Quilt Paste patterned paper (from magazines, etc.) onto a large sheet of paper to make a paper quilt. You could use material if you have it, too.

Red Robot - Rainbows Talk about the colours of the rainbow and then paint one.

Sammy Snake - String & Sequins Make an 's' shape with string, stick it to card with lots of glue, then sprinkle it with sequins for scales so you get a sequiny, stringy Sammy!

Talking Tess - Telescopes Make telescopes with long cardboard tubes from tin foil or kitchen roll. Paint them, or cover them with coloured paper. Fix coloured cellophane (e.g. from sweet wrappers) over the ends with elastic bands, and then see how the world looks!

Uppy Umbrella - Upside-down Game This is an observation game that's quick but fun to play often. From time to time, secretly turn something in the room upside-down. Ask, 'What's unusual now?' See if your friends can spot what is upside-down!

Vicky Violet - Violets Make violets by wrapping violet tissue paper around pipe cleaners for petals. For each violet, tie on five tissue paper leaves, then put them in a vase.

Walter Walrus - Winter Pictures Stick white paper hills and cotton wool snowmen on to coloured paper to make winter scenes. Add a window frame to the pictures using black tape.

Fix-it Max - Boxes Decorate boxes with wrapping paper to give as gifts or put presents in.

Yellow Yo-yo Man - Yellow Collection Collect as many things as you can that are yellow and put them in a box. You could set a time limit for the collection.

Zig Zag Zebra - Zebra Heads Make card headbands and attach black and white ears.

Index

Letterland

Cookbook

An alphabet of recipes

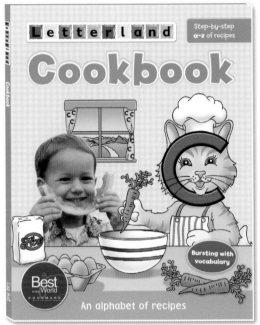

Create delicious desserts and scrumptious savouries with this step-by-step children's cookbook. The simple recipes teach basic cookery skills, introduce children to new vocabulary and teach them to follow instructions - the Letterland way. 48 Pages of culinary fun combined with early literacy skills development.

Child-friendly phonics

See our full range at: **www.letterland.com**

For product advice and support: **info@letterland.com**

Letterland

Child-friendly phonics

The Letterland system teaches all 44 sounds in the English language through stories rather than rules. There are resources to take children from the very first stages of learning to full literacy.

ABC Trilogy

Handwriting Practice

My First & My Second Activity Books

Sticker & Activity Books

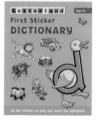

Picture Books

Games & Puzzles

See our full range at: **www.letterland.com**

For product advice and support: **info@letterland.com**